Traveling Bear™

This Book
Belongs to:

_____

Forward

Hello everybody! Welcome to the Traveling Bear Journeys.

The Journey, *Traveling Bear Goes to the Movies*, teaches the importance of setting and achieving goals. Read this journey with your child. At the end, complete the "What's Most Important?" exercise with your child. The purpose of this exercise is to help your child recognize the positive behavioral patterns that are exemplified throughout the journey and motivate your child to go after something special.

Remember, have fun and just find a way to get there!

Visit Traveling Bear at www.travelingbear.com

Traveling Bear™ Goes to the Movies

"Achieving Goals"

Traveling Bear woke up to a rainy day. "Oh, boy!" he said. "What a great movie day! I want to see that new space movie!"

He went downstairs to ask if his mom or dad could drive him to the theater.

"Sorry, T-Bear," said Dad. "We have to leave for the day, but Grandma and Grandpa will stay with you. They'll be over later."

"So how will I get to the movie?" asked Traveling Bear.

"I don't know," said his dad. "You're a smart bear, you'll find a way."

"I know!" said Traveling Bear. "I'll call Mookie and see if her parents can drive us."

"Sorry, T-Bear," said Mookie on the phone. "My mom has to take my little brother somewhere and my dad's not home."

"I'll think of something and call you back!"
said Traveling Bear.

"Oh, no, Dad!" cried Traveling Bear. "I called some of my friends, but their parents can't drive today. They're all busy."

"Let's see," said Dad. "You could take a cab, but that might be really expensive. Or you could walk, but that might take a really long time. Or…."

"I know," said Traveling Bear. "I could take the bus!"

Traveling Bear made a list of all the information he needed—
the movie times, the bus schedule, finding out where the bus
stop was, checking back with Mookie….

Traveling Bear felt overwhelmed. "This is so complicated,"
he said. "How can I do all this?"

Then, Traveling Bear saw an add for the movie in the newspaper.

"Wow!" he said. "The first hundred customers in line get free popcorn!"

That did it. Traveling Bear was determined to find a way to get to the movie.

"All the trouble to get there will be worth it," he said. "Besides, I don't want to disappoint Mookie."

Traveling Bear went to find his dad and tell him he would take the bus.

"I'm proud of you, T-Bear," said Dad. "You set a goal for yourself and, with a little hard work, you'll meet it! That's going to make your day extra special, you'll see."

Traveling Bear found all the information he needed. He wrote everything down so he wouldn't forget. And the bus stop was just a few blocks from his house.

He and Mookie took the bus to the movies, got their free popcorn, and had a great time!

When the movie let out, Traveling Bear turned to his friend. "I know where we have to go to take the bus home."

Suddenly, they heard someone honking at them. "Isn't that your Grandpa?" asked Mookie.

"Hi, you two," said Grandpa from the car. "Anybody need a lift?"

"Thanks a lot," said Traveling Bear. "I can give you bus fare and popcorn!"

"Keep the bus fare," said Grandpa with a wink. "I'll take the popcorn!"

"Wow! What a day . . .

We all know that if you want good things in life to happen to you,

Here's what you need to do... 1, 2, 1 - 2 - 3

Get out of bed I said, get fed, have bread, just find a way to get there.

Travel to school on a mule, on a bike, take a hike, just find a way to get there.

Let out a moan, sing a tone, talk on the phone, just find a way to get there.

On a boat, on a goat, on a plane or on the train, just find a way to get there.

Forget about your hair, so people take a stare, who cares, just find a way to get there!

Bye, everybody!

What's Most Important?

Read the paragraphs below with your child and help him/her circle the words in the parentheses that best complete the sentence.

Traveling Bear woke up to a (**sunny, rainy**) day. He wanted to go to the (**movies, park**). No one was available to drive him there, so Traveling Bear decided to take a (**bus, train**). But getting all the details was (**hard, easy**). When he saw a movie ad in the (**newspaper, magazine**), he decided that it (**was, wasn't**) worth the trouble. Soon, he and (**Mookie, Chuga**) were on a bus heading for the movies. They ended up getting free (**popcorn, candy**) and a ride home from (**Grandpa, Mom**). Traveling Bear set a (**goal, deadline**) for himself and worked hard to achieve it.

He (**found, didn't find**) a way to get there! Do you think that you can set a goal and get there just like (**Traveling Bear, Chuga**)? Give it a try!